REAL LIFE SEA MONSTERS

Giant Squid and Octopuses

by Ruth Owen

PowerKiDS press.

New York

Published in 2014 by The Rosen Publishing Group, Inc.
29 East 21st Street, New York, NY 10010

Produced for Rosen by Ruby Tuesday Books Ltd
Editor for Ruby Tuesday Books Ltd: Mark J. Sachner
US Editor: Joshua Shadowens
Designer: Emma Randall

Photo Credits:
Cover, 1, 4–5, 18–19, 20–21, 28–29 © Shutterstock; 6–7, 11, 12–13, 22–23,
27 © FLPA; 8–9, 24–25 © Superstock; 10 © Science Photo Library;
14–15 © Getty Images; 16–17 © Press Association.

Library of Congress Cataloging-in-Publication Data

Owen, Ruth, 1967–
 Giant squid and octopuses / by Ruth Owen.
     pages cm. — (Real life sea monsters)
 Includes index.
 ISBN 978-1-4777-6261-5 (library) — ISBN 978-1-4777-6262-2 (pbk.) —
 ISBN 978-1-4777-6263-9 (6-pack)
 1. Octopuses—Juvenile literature. 2. Squids—Juvenile literature.
 I. Title.
 QL430.3.O2O937 2014
 594'.56—dc23

                                 2013029147

Manufactured in the United States of America

CPSIA Compliance Information: Batch #W14PK7: For Further Information contact: Rosen Publishing, New York, New York at 1-800-237-9932

CONTENTS

A SEA MONSTER ATTACKS!

A large ship sails on a calm sea. Suddenly, a forest of enormous, arm-like tentacles breaks the surface of the water.

A massive sea creature emerges from the ocean and begins to wrap its tentacles around the ship. The sailors hack at the beast with axes, but they are doomed to a watery death, as the hungry monster pulls their ship beneath the water.

For centuries, people imagined the world's oceans were home to giant sea monsters. Stories of monsters attacking ships were passed down from generation to generation. Today, we know these horrifying creatures do not exist. So how did the terrifying stories of killer sea monsters get started?

Folktales from Norway told of the kraken. This enormous sea monster had horrifying, grasping arms, soccer ball-sized eyes, and powerful jaws.

REAL LIFE SEA MONSTERS

Stories of giant, tentacled sea monsters probably came from sightings of real life animals such as octopuses and squid.

The animal pictured here is a large **species** of squid called the Humboldt, or jumbo, squid. These ocean hunters grow to around 6.5 feet (2 m) in length. Many sea monster tales may have begun with sightings of the truly immense giant squid. There have been reports of these squid growing to lengths of 60 feet (18 m)! An average length for the giant squid, however, is 40 feet (12 m).

Humboldt squid have been photographed and studied in the world's oceans. No one had ever photographed a live giant squid in its natural habitat, however, until 2004!

A Humboldt squid

Scientists have discovered most of what they know about giant squid by studying dead giant squid that wash up on beaches.

GIANT SQUID PHYSICAL FACTS

Squid are invertebrates, which means they are animals without a backbone.

A giant squid has a combined head and body called a mantle. At one end of the mantle are the animal's fins. At the other end are eight powerful arms and two extremely long tentacles.

A giant squid's arms can grow to be over 9 feet (3 m) long. Some especially large giant squid may have tentacles that are up to 40 feet (12 m) long.

The giant squid's record-breaking total-length measurement includes its mantle and its tentacles. These huge animals can reach weights of 880 to 2,000 pounds (400–900 kg).

A Humboldt squid eye

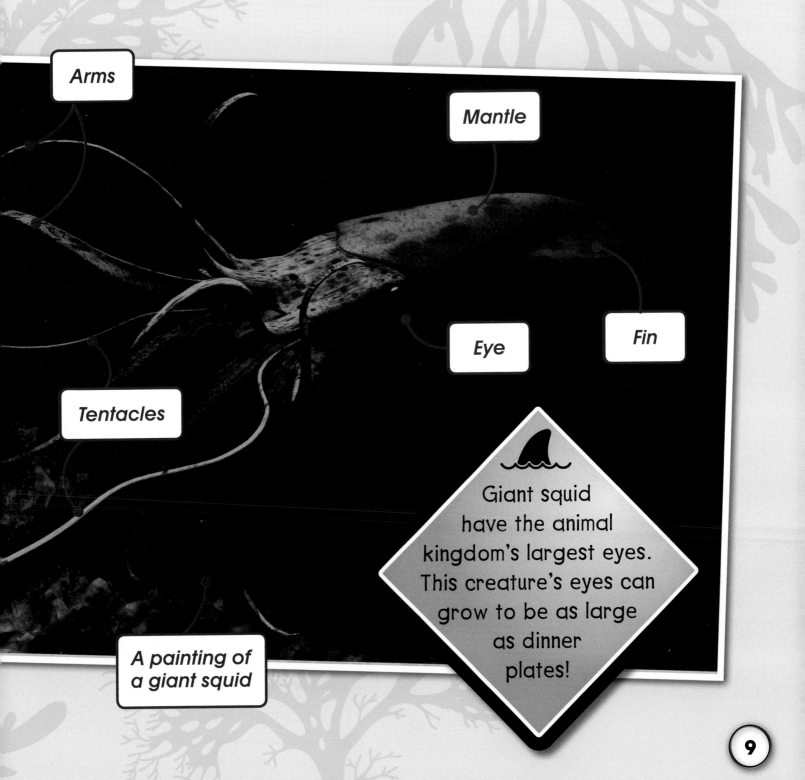

Arms

Mantle

Eye

Fin

Tentacles

A painting of
a giant squid

Giant squid
have the animal
kingdom's largest eyes.
This creature's eyes can
grow to be as large
as dinner
plates!

A GIANT HUNTER

Scientists believe giant squid only live for about five years. In order to get so large, these animals have to grow fast. To grow fast, giant squid must catch and eat vast quantities of fish and other squid.

A giant squid catches its **prey** with body parts called clubs on the ends of its tentacles. Suckers on the animal's clubs, tentacles, and arms attach to the prey and hold on with powerful suction.

Once its prey is trapped, the squid pulls its meal toward its mantle. The squid's arms help hold the struggling creature and drag it into the squid's sharp, parrot-like beak.

A squid's beak is inside the mantle. The sharp beak easily breaks the prey animal into small pieces.

A giant squid's beak

Suckers

Circles of sharp, teeth-like chitin

Inside a squid's suckers are rings of a hard substance called **chitin** that sink into its victim's flesh like sharp teeth.

MEGA BATTLES

Giant squid are among the largest predators that live in the world's oceans. These huge predators have their own enormous enemies, though.

A giant squid's main predators are sperm whales. Weighing many tons (t) and growing longer than school buses, sperm whales travel the world's oceans hunting giant squid. Their prey, however, do not give up without a fight! Many sperm whales carry the scars, including large sucker marks, of their mega battles with giant squid.

Sperm whales have helped scientists find out about giant squid. The whales cannot digest the squids' hard beaks. When whales are washed up on beaches, and scientists examine their stomach contents, the scientists often find giant squid beaks that can then be studied.

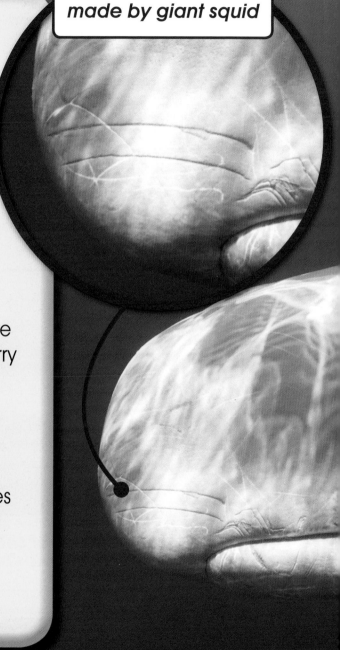

A close-up of scars made by giant squid

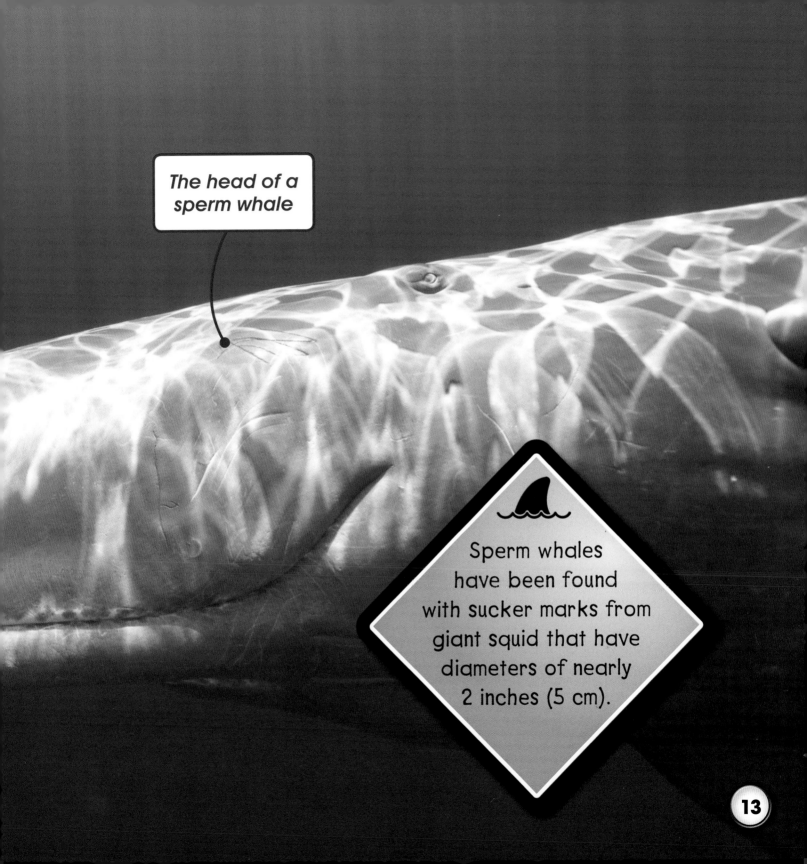

The head of a
sperm whale

Sperm whales
have been found
with sucker marks from
giant squid that have
diameters of nearly
2 inches (5 cm).

13

MEET ARCHIE

Fishing boats sometimes accidentally catch giant squid in their nets. In 2004, a giant squid was caught near the Falkland Islands in the South Atlantic Ocean.

The enormous **specimen**, nicknamed Archie, was frozen and transported to the Natural History Museum in London. Scientists at the museum decided not to **dissect** Archie, but to preserve the squid whole.

It took three days for Archie to defrost. Then scientists unraveled the squid's tentacles and measured the animal. Finally, Archie was put on display in a super-long tank of water. The water contains salt and a chemical called formalin, which will preserve the squid's body.

ENCOUNTER WITH A GIANT

In 2004, Japanese scientist Tsunemi Kubodera and his team became the first people to capture photos of a live giant squid in its natural habitat.

At a depth of nearly half a mile (0.9 km) beneath the ocean, the scientists used a long fishing line baited with food that is attractive to giant squid. As a huge squid attacked the bait, underwater cameras took more than 500 photos of the creature. The team estimated that the giant squid measured about 25 feet (7.6 m) long.

The Japanese team had decided to follow sperm whales. They hoped the whales would lead them to places where the team could find the mysterious giant squid. Their plan worked!

In 2006, Tsunemi Kubodera and his team achieved another first. They became the first people to catch and film a live giant squid.

Tsunemi Kubodera

Mantle

Giant squid

THE GIANT OCTOPUS

Along with huge squid, the world's oceans are home to another long-armed monster, the giant Pacific octopus.

There are around 300 different species of octopus. The giant Pacific octopus is the largest. Its arm span may stretch up to 30 feet (9 m)!

These real life sea monsters have a special skill. They can disguise themselves. To help it hide from predators, a giant octopus can change its skin color to blend in with its background. An octopus's skin contains thousands of tiny sacs filled with colored dye. Muscles around the sacs allow the octopus to enlarge the sacs or squeeze them tight to make different colors appear or disappear.

A giant Pacific octopus

A giant Pacific octopus can even change its skin **texture** from smooth to bumpy to blend in with its surroundings and hide from enemies.

GIANT OCTOPUS PHYSICAL FACTS

Octopuses and squid are related sea creatures. Like squid, octopuses are invertebrates and have no bones in their bodies.

Also, like squid, octopuses have a combined head and body called a mantle. Octopuses have eight strong arms that they use for grabbing things. Each arm has two rows of suckers.

Octopuses breathe using body parts called **gills**. They suck water into their gills, take **oxygen** out of the water, and then blow the water out through a tube called a funnel.

Between an octopus's arms there is skin called a web. An octopus can suck water into its web and then quickly shoot the water out. This blast of water can propel the octopus along, fast!

A giant Pacific octopus's arm

Suckers

Mantle

Web

Arms

An octopus can use its suckers to taste the things it touches.

FEEDING TIME

Giant octopuses catch and eat fish, crabs, and shellfish. They use their suckers to rip apart prey such as crabs.

Like squid, octopuses have hard beaks that they use for biting into their food. An octopus can also inject its prey with chemicals that poison the animal and soften its meat for eating.

Giant octopuses make dens among rocks. Inside a den, an octopus can eat and rest, safe from predators. After a meal, an octopus will dump trash, such as crab shells, outside the den's entrance. It uses water jets from its funnel to sweep its leftovers out of the den.

Sometimes fish visit the entrance to an octopus's den looking for a snack of octopus leftovers.

A dead shark, found on the seabed, is a feast for a hungry octopus.

ESCAPE TACTICS

A giant Pacific octopus is a large predator, but it still has predators of its own, such as sharks and other large fish.

Like most other octopus species, a giant Pacific octopus can release a cloud of thick black ink from its body if a predator gets too close. The ink spreads through the water so the predator's view of the octopus is blocked. Then the octopus makes its escape.

An octopus's ink also contains a substance that keeps the predator's sense of smell from working very well. This is important when avoiding sharks and other predators that use smell to find their food.

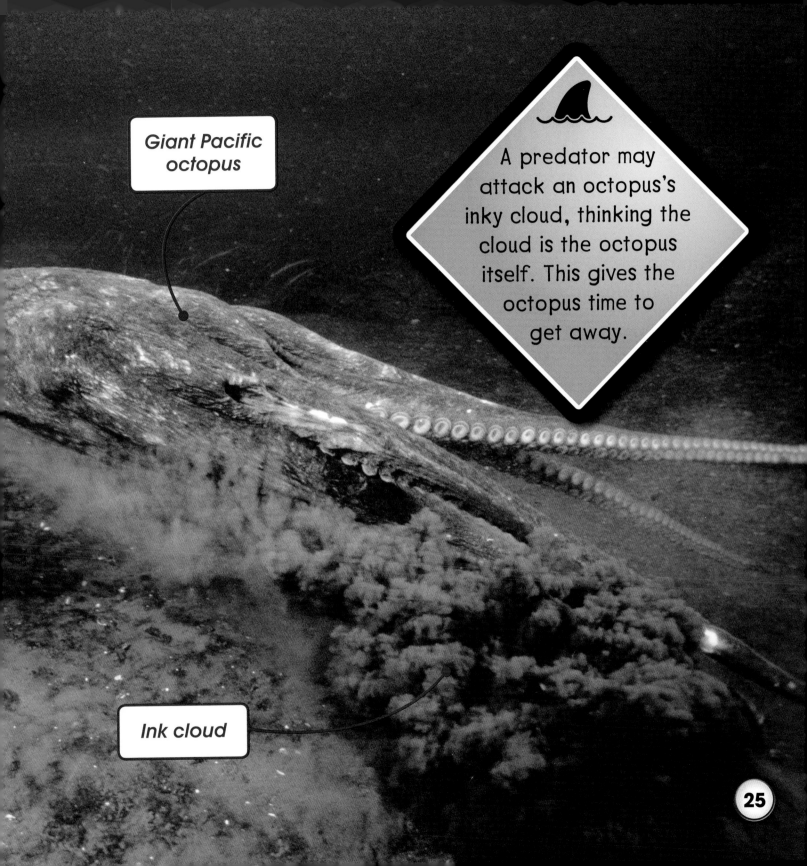

Giant Pacific octopus

A predator may attack an octopus's inky cloud, thinking the cloud is the octopus itself. This gives the octopus time to get away.

Ink cloud

SEA MONSTER MOTHERS

Female giant Pacific octopuses are very caring moms that actually give their lives to make sure their eggs hatch!

After mating, a female giant octopus finds a safe den and lays her eggs. She uses her saliva, or spit, to connect her eggs into strings. Then she sticks the strings to the roof of her den.

The female octopus watches over her eggs for six and a half months. She guards the eggs from predators such as crabs and sea stars. While she is waiting for her eggs to hatch, she doesn't hunt or eat. Once the baby octopuses hatch and swim away, the female octopus dies.

A female giant Pacific octopus lays around 57,000 eggs.

Strings of eggs

Female giant Pacific octopus in den

27

THE SMARTEST SEA MONSTER

One thing that scientists have discovered over the years by studying octopuses in aquariums is that these animals are very smart!

Octopuses have been trained to find their way through mazes and tell the difference between squares and crosses.

Octopuses can also learn to carry out tasks such as unscrewing the lid of a jar to get to some food. An octopus named Ruby at the Biomes Marine Biology Center in Rhode Island was given a jar without a lid that contained a crab. Then, he was given a jar with a loose lid. As Ruby learned how to turn the lid, it was tightened. Ruby quickly learned to unscrew the lid to get to his crab treat!

Keepers in aquariums say that octopuses recognize the keepers' faces and will come out of their dens to beg for food.

GLOSSARY

aquariums (uh-KWAYR-ee-umz) Places where animals that live in water are kept for study and show.

chitin (KY-tin) A hard, natural material that forms the beaks of squid. It is the main material in the shells of insects, and the shells of crustaceans such as crabs and lobsters.

dissect (DY-sekt) To cut an animal or plant into pieces so that it can be scientifically studied.

folktales (FOHK-taylz) Stories passed down from generation to generation, usually by people telling the stories rather than writing them down. Folktales are often based on real-life events or explain something that happens in nature.

gills (GILZ) Body parts that underwater animals use for breathing. The gills take oxygen out of water and send it into an animal's body.

invertebrates (in-VER-teh-brets) Animals that have no backbone. This animal group includes ocean animals such as squid and octopuses, and land animals such as insects, which have hard outer shells instead of bony skeletons, as well as worms and snails.

oxygen (OK-sih-jen) The gas that humans and other animals need to breathe.

predators (PREH-duh-terz) Animals that hunt and kill other animals for food.

prey (PRAY) Animals that are hunted by other animals as food.

species (SPEE-sheez) One type of living thing. The members of a species look alike and can produce young together.

specimen (SPES-menz) A sample of something or an item to be scientifically studied.

tentacles (TEN-tih-kulz) Long, arm-like body parts.

texture (TEKS-chur) The way that the surface of something looks or feels. For example, smooth, rough, bumpy, or spiky are types of textures.

WEBSITES

Due to the changing nature of Internet links, PowerKids Press has developed an online list of websites related to the subject of this book. This site is updated regularly. Please use this link to access the list:

www.powerkidslinks.com/rlsm/squid/

READ MORE

Cerullo, Mary M. *Giant Squid: Searching for a Sea Monster*. Mankato, MN: Capstone Press, 2012.

Miller, Tori. *Octopuses and Squid*. Freaky Fish. New York: PowerKids Press, 2009.

Shea, Therese. *The Bizarre Life Cycle of Octopuses*. Strange Life Cycles. New York: Gareth Stevens Learning Library, 2012.

INDEX